DISNEY's Year Book 2004

FERN L. MAMBERG   *Executive Editor*
ELIZABETH A. DeBELLA   *Designer*
KATHERINE M. SIEPIETOSKI   *Production Manager*

Articles designed by Northwoods Design Group
Stories and crafts illustrated by K. White Studio

ISBN: 0-7172-6877-2
ISSN: 0273-1274

Illustration Credits and Acknowledgments

6: American Philosophical Society; The Granger Collection; The Granger Collection; American Philosophical Society. 7: American Philosophical Society; American Philosophical Society; Artist, Gary Torrisi. 8: www. lewisandclarktrail.com; © Georgiana Harbeson/PicturesNow.com. 9: The Granger Collection. 10: © Frans Lanting/Minden Pictures. 11: © Zig Leszczynski/Animals Animals; © Rob Griffith/AP/Wide World Photos. 12: © Joe McDonald/Bruce Coleman Inc.; © Joe McDonald/DRK Photo. 13: © Dwight R. Kuhn; © Dwight R. Kuhn; © Art Wolfe. 28-29: © Phil Schermeister/National Geographic Image Collection. 30: © David M. Grossman/Photo Researchers, Inc.; © Phil Schermeister/National Geographic Image Collection. 31: © Phil Schermeister/National Geographic Image Collection. 32: © Massimo Borchi, Atlantide/Bruce Coleman Inc. 33: © Billy Hustace/Stone/Getty Images. 46: © Ron Gordon Garrison/Zoological Society of San Diego. 47: © Dennis Demello/Wildlife Conservation Society; © The San Francisco Zoological Society; © Dennis Demello/Wildlife Conservation Society. 48: Robert Harbison/© The Christian Science Monitor (www. csmonitor.com), all rights reserved. 49: © Frans Lanting/Minden Pictures. 50: © Edwin Giesbers. 51: © Fritz Polking/Bruce Coleman Inc.; © Nick Garbutt/naturpl.com; © Dennis MacDonald/PhotoEdit; © Michael Fogden/Bruce Coleman Inc./PictureQuest; © Michael Fogden/DRK Photo. 52: © Phil A. Dotson/ Photo Researchers, Inc.; © Bruce Coleman Inc./PictureQuest. 53: © Ulrike Welsch/PhotoEdit; © Janice Sheldon/Photo 20-20/PictureQuest. 68: Superstock. 69: © Giorgio Gualco/Bruce Coleman Inc.; Superstock; © Coco McCoy/Rainbow/PictureQuest. 70: © Melloan/PhotoEdit; © Adam Woolfitt/Woodfin Camp & Associates. 71: Don Cole/UCLA Fowler Museum of Cultural History. 72: © Gerard Lacz/Animals Animals; © F. J. Hiersche/Okapia/Photo Researchers, Inc. 73: © Sid Bahrt/Photo Researchers, Inc.; © Tui De Roy/Bruce Coleman Inc.; © C. K. Lorenz/Photo Researchers, Inc. 86: © Adam Butler/AP/Wide World Photos. 87: © Steve Holland/AP/Wide World Photos; © Adam Butler/AP/Wide World Photos. 88: © Paul Harris/Online USA/Getty Images; © Steve Holland/ AP/Wide World Photos; © Mark Lennihan/ AP/Wide World Photos. 89: © Amy E. Conn/AP/Wide World Photos; © Getty Images. 90: © Dave B. Fleetham/Tom Stack & Associates; © Fred Bavendam. 91: © Denise Tackett/Tom Stack & Associates; © Larry Lipsky/DRK Photo. 92: © Juergen & Christine Sohns/Animals Animals; © Stephen J. Krasemann/ DRK Photo. 93: © G. Hinde, ABPL/Animals Animals; © K&K Ammann/Bruce Coleman Inc. 94: © Fred Bavendam/Minden Pictures; © Fred Bavendam. 95: © Michael Fogden/DRK Photo.

Disney's Year Book 2004

SCHOLASTIC INC.

New York • Toronto • London • Auckland • Sydney •
Mexico City • New Delhi • Hong Kong • Buenos Aires

Contents

Meriwether Lewis (left) and William Clark (right) explored the West in 1804-06. Their journals, which included drawings, described everything they found.

Lewis & Clark:
A Great Adventure

In 1804 a band of explorers began a great trip across the western United States. Back then, no one was sure what lay between the Mississippi River and the Pacific Ocean. The explorers knew only that the voyage of discovery would be long and hard—and dangerous!

Meriwether Lewis and William Clark led the expedition. Thanks to them, Americans learned about the wonders of the West. This year marks the 200th anniversary of their trip. It was a great adventure!

Lewis and Clark found lots of new plants in the West. These two plants were named for them—*Lewisii* (left) and *Clarkia* (right).

This looks like duckweed to me!

The trip was President Thomas Jefferson's idea. Jefferson hoped Lewis and Clark would find a way to reach the Pacific Ocean by boat. He also wanted them to learn everything they could about the West.

Lewis and Clark left St. Louis, Missouri, on May 14, 1804. With them were about 30 soldiers. They headed up the Missouri River in boats. The long journey had begun.

Lewis and Clark's Journey West

Lewis and Clark gave medals like this to Indian leaders. The medal shows President Thomas Jefferson on one side. The other side shows a handshake of friendship.

The explorers paddled upriver for many miles. They saw all kinds of animals—prairie dogs . . . and bison . . . and grizzly bears! And they met many American Indians, who often helped them.

Lewis and Clark spent the winter near an Indian village in what is today North Dakota. In the spring, they headed upriver again. Ahead lay miles and miles of flat plains. And beyond the plains were the tall Rocky Mountains.

To cross the mountains, Lewis and Clark had to leave their boats. They traveled on foot, with horses carrying their gear. They nearly ran out of food. But they made it!

Sacagawea

Sacagawea (sak-a-ja-WE-a) was the only woman on the journey. She was the wife of a trapper who was hired as a guide. And she was a remarkable person!

Sacagawea was a Shoshoni Indian. She spoke several Indian languages. She helped the explorers talk and trade with the Indians they met. And she helped them get horses for the trip over the Rocky Mountains.

Sacagawea carried her newborn son with her. Seeing a woman and a baby, the Indians knew that the travelers were peaceful. They let them pass.

Pictures from an 1811 book show events along the trail: A bear chases a hunter up a tree. The explorers build huts. Lewis and Clark meet with Indians. A canoe tips over.

Let's go out west for an adventure!

Beyond the mountains, Lewis and Clark stopped to make new boats. Then they headed down a series of rivers. In November 1805 they reached the Pacific Ocean!

The explorers spent the winter on the Pacific Coast, in present-day Oregon. Then they made the long trip home, back over the mountains and across the plains. They reached St. Louis in September 1806. They were greeted as heroes, and they told everyone about the wonders they had seen. And soon many other explorers and settlers headed west.

ANIMAL MAGICIANS

The chameleon is famous because it can change color. But it is amazing in other ways, too!

Chameleons are animal magicians. They can change color! And that's not the only trick these animals can do.

Chameleons are lizards. There are about 90 different kinds. Some are longer than your arm. Others are smaller than your thumb. They make their homes in warm places, mostly in Africa and Asia.

Most chameleons are green or brown. Some may have yellow, blue, red, and black on their bodies, too. But their colors and patterns can change in the blink of an eye!

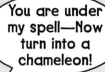

You are under my spell—Now turn into a chameleon!

Like other lizards, chameleons hatch from eggs.

The chameleon's trick isn't really magic. Sometimes a change in temperature or light causes the color change. Warmth and sunlight darken the lizard's colors. Coolness and shade make the colors lighter.

Moods can also make these animals change their hues. When a chameleon is scared, its colors are dull. When it's angry, its colors are dark.

Some chameleons are only a couple of inches long. And some are a couple of feet long!

A chameleon has a secret weapon: its loooong, sticky-tipped tongue! The hungry chameleon shoots out its tongue to catch an insect—and swallows it whole!

Males may change color to attract mates. Rival males even have color wars. They face off and try to scare each other, turning bright colors!

How does a chameleon perform this trick? Its skin has layers of color cells. The cells in each layer have different pigments—chemicals that create color. Light, warmth, and moods affect the cells, so the pigments shift.

Here's another chameleon trick. This lizard can look in two different directions at once. One eye can look forward, while the other eye looks back.

Chameleons are amazing in still other ways. A chameleon's tongue may be as long as its body!

Most chameleons live in trees. They use their grasping claws to climb. Their long tails help, too. A chameleon can grip with its tail. Most of the time, the tail stays coiled up. But when the chameleon needs to hang on extra tight, it wraps its tail around a branch.

This animal magician knows LOTS of tricks!

Shade makes a chameleon go pale. When a fern leaf is taken off a chameleon's back (above), a pale "print" is left behind.

Did You Know?

A chameleon's bulging eyes are covered by scaly lids. The eyes can move in two different directions at the same time!

The Sticky Honey Pot

"Oh, fluff and stuff!" said Pooh in an echo-y sort of voice. You see, Pooh had gotten his head stuck in a pot of honey while trying to lick the very last bit of the sticky sweet stuff from the bottom of the pot. Now Pooh's head had been stuck in honey pots before, where it would remain until he managed to twist and wiggle himself free . . . or until someone came along to pull the pot off for him.

Right now, however, Pooh was really in a lot of trouble. His head was wedged quite tightly, and there was no one around. So he decided to look for help. Unfortunately, having a pot on one's head makes looking for others somewhat difficult.

Bump! Thump!

"Oh, double bother!" Pooh said inside the pot. The bump had been made by his bumping into something in his house. The thump had been the sound of his backside landing on the floor immediately after the bump.

How was Pooh going to find someone to help him? Then he had an idea. This made Pooh rather proud, as bears of very little brain don't often have ideas.

"I shall find my way outside, where someone will find me!" he decided.

Feeling very pleased with himself, Pooh managed to figure a way (with a few more bumps and thumps) to move across the room to his open door.

"Lovely," Pooh said to himself (only it sounded more like "lumply" from inside the honey pot). "Now I shall simply wait for someone to rescue me." And so he did.

Pooh waited and waited. And waited. He tried
humming to himself but got confused by the echoes, so
he stopped. Then he tried tapping his foot, but that
didn't seem to be all that interesting. At last, Pooh fell
asleep.

After a bit, Pooh's good friend Piglet came by for a
visit. When Piglet saw his friend sitting on a tree
stump outside his door with a honey pot on his head
and making a strange noise, he was puzzled.

"Pooh?" asked Piglet tentatively.

"Mmmmmmmm-pffff. Mmmmmmm-pffffff," said
Pooh.

"Oh, did I interrupt your lunch?" asked Piglet.
"Perhaps I should come back later."

"Um-hmmmm." Pooh was snoring, but Piglet thought
Pooh had said "Uh-huh," as in, "Yes, please do return

later." So Piglet left without Pooh ever even knowing he had been there.

Soon after, Tigger arrived at Pooh's house.

"Hiya, Pooh Bear!" Tigger bounced atop Pooh.

"Oof! Oof!" said Pooh. To Tigger, it sounded as if Pooh had said "Hoo-hoo!"

"That's right, Pooh Boy!" cried Tigger. "I say that, too. Only sometimes I add an extra 'HOO!' to make it extra-specially tiggery. Hoo-hoo-HOO!"

Pooh didn't hear a thing Tigger was saying. He was simply trying to catch his breath after being bounced.

"Well," said Tigger. "I got some more bouncin' ta do. See ya later, Pooh Bear. Hoo-hoo-HOO!"

Tigger bounced Pooh one last time before he left, leading Pooh to say once again, "Oof!" This delighted Tigger, as he believed Pooh was talking to him.

Soon evening fell, and Pooh stumbled inside his house and closed the door. He sat down in his comfy chair, wondering if someone might still come to

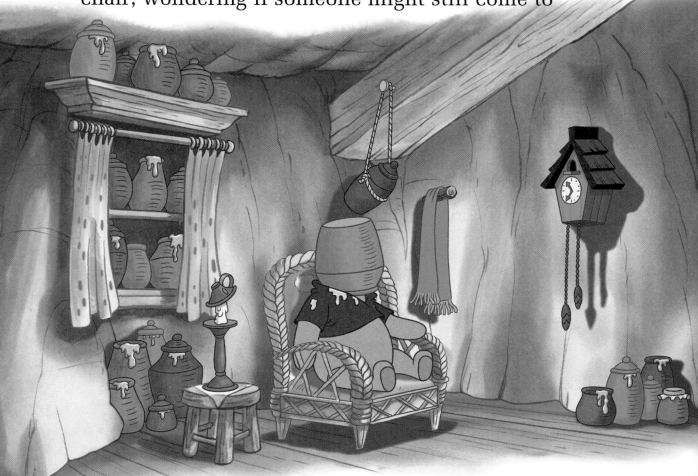

rescue him. He was hoping that the someone might come sooner rather than later. His rumbly tummy was telling him it was way past both tea and supper time.

At last there came a loud rapping at Pooh's door, which, of course, Pooh couldn't hear at all.

Christopher Robin popped his head inside Pooh's front door and found his favorite bear sitting quietly in his comfy chair with a honey pot wedged tightly over his head.

"Oh, Pooh, you silly old bear!" said Christopher Robin playfully. "I've been looking everywhere for you. I haven't seen you all day, and I thought—"

Christopher Robin suddenly stopped talking. He realized that Pooh could probably not hear a word he was saying. So he went over to Pooh and tapped very gently on the honey pot.

Pooh sat up straight and shouted, "Come on in!" He
thought someone was knocking at his
door. All Christopher Robin
heard was, "Kooo-eeee!"

Christopher Robin had
seen Pooh stuck in this type
of situation before. He
began to twist and turn the
pot ever so gently to try to
get it off Pooh's head. But
no matter which way he

twisted, turned, and
pulled at the honey
pot, it simply
would not
budge.

   Then he got
an idea. He
went over to
Pooh's kitchen sink
and got a cloth and
dipped it into some warm, soapy water. Carefully
he wiped away the gooey honey that was sticking
all around Pooh's head and neck.
After a while, Christopher
Robin gave one last
yank on the honey
pot.

Pop!

Off came the pot, and out popped Pooh's head.

"Oh, hello, Christopher Robin!" Pooh said excitedly. "I was hoping you might come by. You see, I have this pot stuck on my head, and I thought you might be able to help me get it off."

"Silly old bear!" said Christopher Robin. "Look! It's already off your head! That's why you can see me and hear me!"

"Oh," said Pooh. "Well, in that case, thank you very much for your help!"

So, feeling rather generous and grateful, Pooh asked
Christopher Robin to stay for supper with him.
Christopher Robin gladly accepted, and the two good
friends had a wonderful evening.

And when Pooh began to look at the bottom of his
honey pot to finish off the very
last smackerel of his delicious
supper, Christopher Robin
made sure that the bear
used his paw instead
of his head to
get it!

Fantasy Flowers

These pretty fantasy flowers are made from colorful tissue paper. They are fun to make. You can keep them or give them to a special person.

What You Need

White Glue

Tissue Paper (lots of colors, including black)

Florist Wire

Scissors

Green Florist Tape

What You Do

1. Crumple up a small piece of green tissue paper. Glue it onto one end of a piece of wire. This will be the center of the flower.

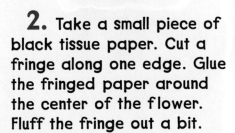

2. Take a small piece of black tissue paper. Cut a fringe along one edge. Glue the fringed paper around the center of the flower. Fluff the fringe out a bit.

3. Cut out three or four round circles of colorful tissue paper. Scallop the edges of each one. These are the petals. Poke a small hole in the center of each petal.

4. Thread each petal onto the wire, from the bottom up. Push it up to the base of the fringed paper.

5. Wrap the green florist tape around the wire. Start at the top of the wire, below the petals.

Make lots of colored flowers. Place them in a vase and you'll have a rainbow bouquet!

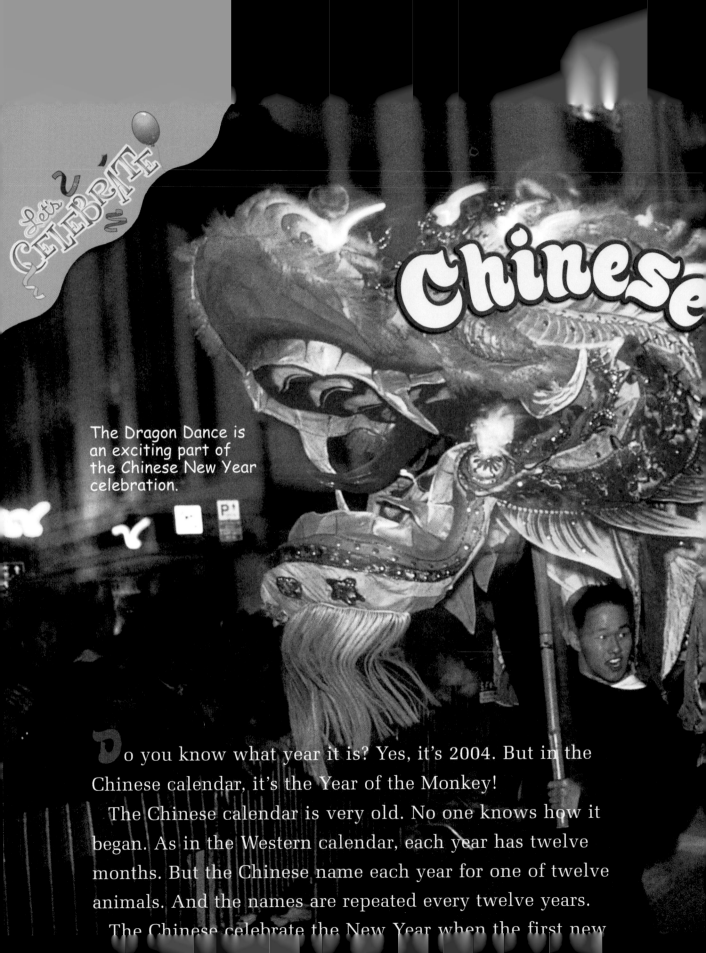

Chinese

The Dragon Dance is an exciting part of the Chinese New Year celebration.

Do you know what year it is? Yes, it's 2004. But in the Chinese calendar, it's the Year of the Monkey!

The Chinese calendar is very old. No one knows how it began. As in the Western calendar, each year has twelve months. But the Chinese name each year for one of twelve animals. And the names are repeated every twelve years.

The Chinese celebrate the New Year when the first new

New Year

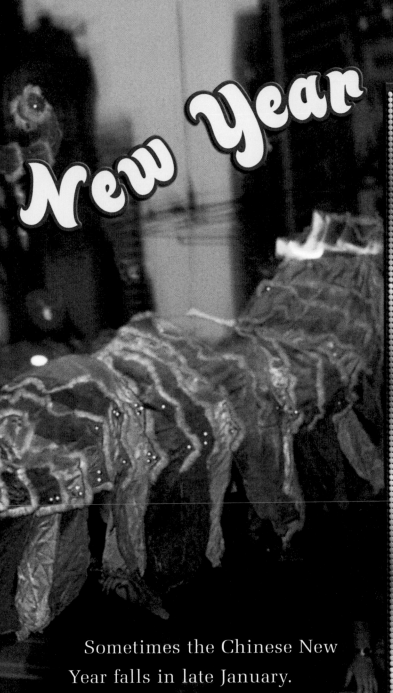

Sometimes the Chinese New Year falls in late January. Sometimes it's in February. But it's always a time for lots of fun. People spend weeks getting ready for this holiday. They buy new clothes. And they clean their houses from top to bottom.

Kitchen God's Day

A picture of the Kitchen God hangs in many Chinese homes. All year, this god is said to watch the family. Then, at the end of the year, the Kitchen God returns to heaven. There he reports everything the family has done to the Jade Emperor, the ruler of heaven.

Kitchen God's Day comes a week before the Chinese New Year. On this day, the god's picture is taken down. Firecrackers are set off to send the god on his way to heaven. But before he goes, the family may brush his lips with honey—so he will have only sweet things to say about the family!

The Kitchen God's place stands empty until New Year's Eve. Then the family hangs up a new picture to welcome him back.

The Kitchen God

Chinese Zodiac

Each year in the Chinese calendar is named for an animal. Tradition says that a person's animal sign shows his or her character. Find your animal sign by looking for your birth year below. Does your character match your sign?

Then the New Year holiday begins—with a bang! On New Year's Eve firecrackers go off. The loud noises are meant to scare away bad spirits.

The holiday fun goes on for days. Families get together. They give gifts and share delicious feasts. Food is set out to honor the family ancestors. There are lots of special New Year's foods, such as sweet rice pudding.

Chinese children are given "good luck" money for the New Year. The money is put in red envelopes. Red is thought to be the luckiest color. The Chinese writing on the envelopes means good wishes.

Monkey
(2004, 1992)
You are clever and charming. You love adventure. And sometimes you get in trouble!

Sheep
(2003, 1991)
You are gentle and a little baa-shful. You are also creative and a good friend.

Horse
(2002, 1990)
You are cheerful, helpful, loyal, and smart. But sometimes you talk too much!

Many of the foods carry meanings. For example, long noodles stand for long life.

Lots of traditions are linked to the Chinese New Year. Most are meant to bring good luck in the year ahead. Knives are put away. They might "cut" someone's luck. And people don't wash their hair on New Year's Day. That might wash away good luck!

I'll put away my sword on New Year's Day so I won't "cut" my luck!

Did You Know?

Sweet foods that are eaten on New Year's Day are said to bring a sweet year.

Snake
(2001)
You are a quiet one, but you are ssssmart. You are also artistic and full of energy.

Dragon
(2000)
You are lucky, healthy, and brave. But your temper can be fiery!

Rabbit
(1999)
You are talented, and you want to get ahead. If there's something to do, you hop to it!

31

The Lion Dance

The Lion Dance is a high point of any New Year celebration. Two dancers bring the lion to life. One is at the front end, working the head. The other is at the back. Together, they make the lion leap and dance through the streets. Three musicians go along. They play a drum, cymbals, and a gong. A well-performed Lion Dance is said to bring good luck.

Dragons are said to bring good luck, too. People line the streets to watch the Dragon Dance. In this colorful parade, dancers carry a long paper dragon through the streets. Another New Year favorite is the Lion Dance.

For everyone, the New Year is a time for fresh starts. Old debts are paid. Even old arguments are forgotten when the New Year begins. Tradition says that enemies must forgive and forget. Everyone must be friends— at least for the first week of the year!

Tiger
(1998)
You are friendly and thoughtful. You also have courage—and can roar!

Ox
(1997)
You are a calm and patient leader. You are strong and always pull your weight!

Rat
(1996)
You are charming and creative. But sometimes you have a quick temper!

The Lantern Festival

The New Year is the most important holiday in China. And it's celebrated in countries all over the world. Wherever Chinese people have settled, they enjoy this special time. In the United States, there are big parades in the Chinatowns of New York City, San Francisco, and other cities. People gather to celebrate. They shout "Gung Hay Fat Choy"—Happy New Year!

Dragons bring good luck!

The Lantern Festival marks the end of the Chinese New Year season. Children carry beautiful colored lanterns through the streets. More lanterns hang on homes and temples. There are fireworks, dancing, and plenty of other fun.

Where's the Year of the Cricket?!

Pig
(1995)
You are brave and strong. You are kind and loving, too. You are never a hog!

Dog
(1994)
You are loyal, funny, and honest. You are the leader of the pack!

Rooster
(1993)
You are confident. You like to crow! But your friends can count on you.

33

The Bird-Sitters

"And this, Simba, is precisely why I ask you to stay close to me!" Zazu said. "Just look around you!"

Simba hung his head, then made himself look around. He and Nala were surrounded by a herd of elephants—angry elephants that had been stampeding just moments ago. Zazu flapped his wings, then perched on the elephant leader's head, just between his long, floppy ears.

"I didn't mean to make them run, Zazu," Simba said. "Honest. Nala and I were playing tag, and I guess they just misunderstood."

Zazu flew in front of Simba to look him in the eye. "Yelling, 'Run for your life!' had nothing to do with it?"

"We were just joking, Zazu," said Nala.

"We'll be more careful," Simba promised. "Um, you won't tell my dad will you, Zazu?"

"Hmm," Zazu ruffled his feathers. "Well, I suppose I could do you a favor if . . ."

"If what?" said Simba.

"Well," Zazu said, "it just so happens that my young niece Zinga will be visiting tomorrow while I have important business with the king. If you'll apologize to the elephants and if you'll bird-sit tomorrow, I suppose I could keep this matter just between us."

Simba turned to the leader of the elephant herd. "I'm sorry," he said. "I won't let it happen again." To Nala, he whispered, "And bird-sitting will be a cinch!"

The next morning, Zazu met Simba and Nala near Pride Rock.

"This is Zinga," said Zazu.

A blur of colors zoomed past Simba and Nala. "That *was* Zinga," said Zazu. "Better catch up with her!"

"But Zazu—" Simba began.

"Just don't leave the Pride Lands," Zazu called as he flew off. "And meet me here at midday. Zinga's mother will be back then."

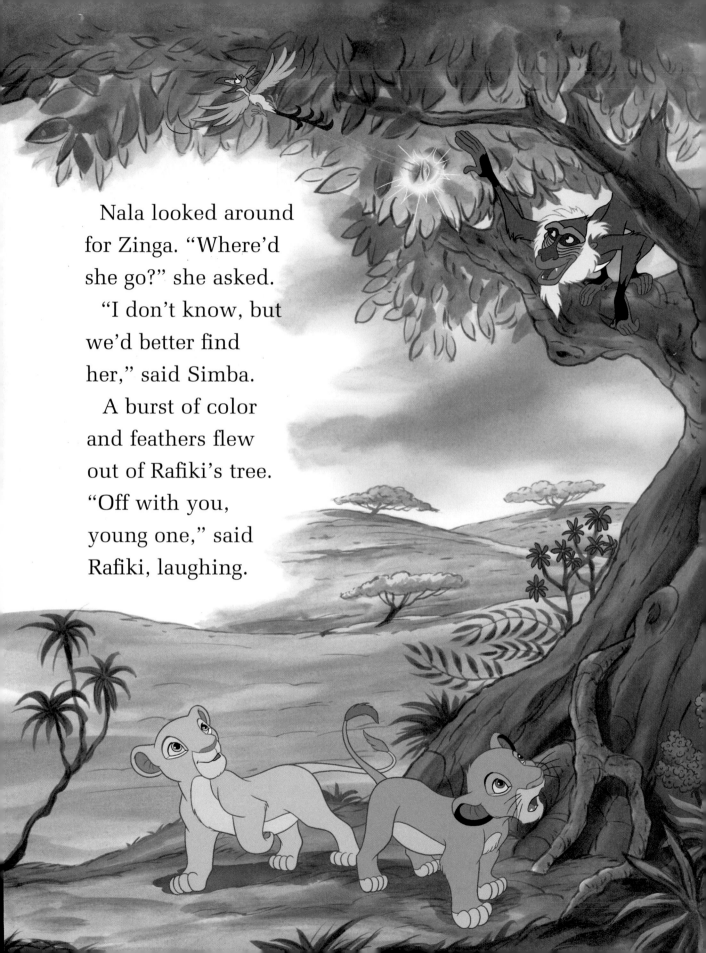

Nala looked around for Zinga. "Where'd she go?" she asked.

"I don't know, but we'd better find her," said Simba.

A burst of color and feathers flew out of Rafiki's tree. "Off with you, young one," said Rafiki, laughing.

"There she goes!" Simba yelled. "Zinga!"

Zinga made a sudden sharp turn and flew straight toward Simba and Nala. She landed on Nala's back, then walked up to her head and perched there. "You must be the bird-sitters. Well, I already told Uncle Zazu I don't need bird-sitters. Ta!" Zinga took off again.

"Where are you going?" Simba ran after her.

"Just out to play!" Zinga called.

"Oh." Simba said. He stopped running. "I guess that doesn't sound so bad."

"Uh, Simba," said Nala, "isn't that what we usually say?"

Simba thought about it. They'd just been playing when they started the elephant stampede. "OH," he called, starting to run again. "Zinga, wait!"

Zinga didn't wait. She flew into a herd of zebras, dodging in and out of their stripes.

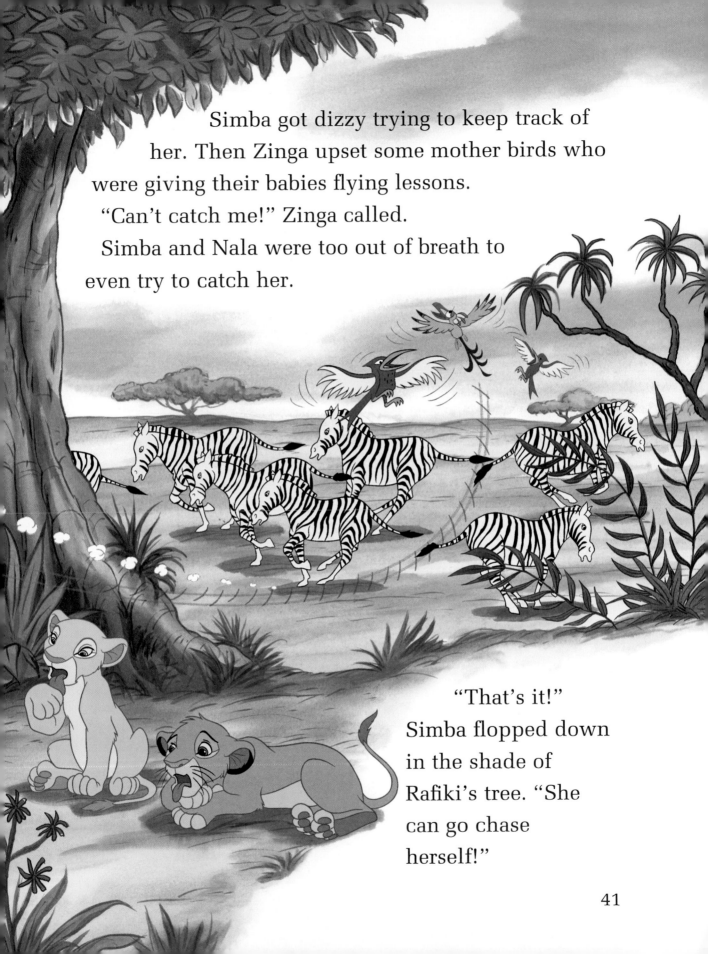

Simba got dizzy trying to keep track of her. Then Zinga upset some mother birds who were giving their babies flying lessons.

"Can't catch me!" Zinga called.

Simba and Nala were too out of breath to even try to catch her.

"That's it!" Simba flopped down in the shade of Rafiki's tree. "She can go chase herself!"

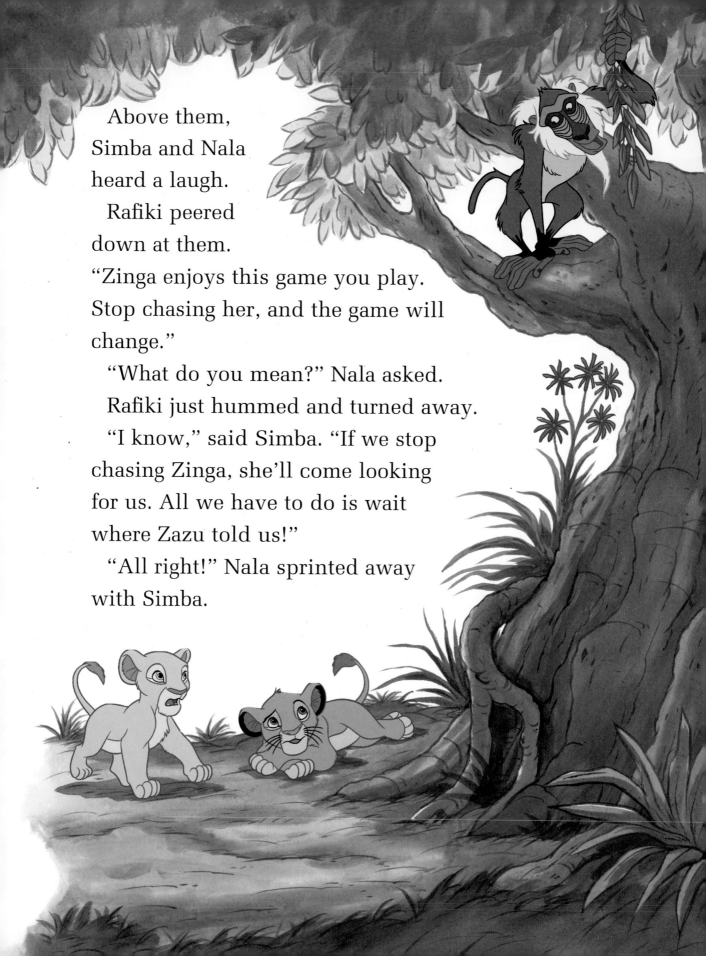

Above them, Simba and Nala heard a laugh.

Rafiki peered down at them. "Zinga enjoys this game you play. Stop chasing her, and the game will change."

"What do you mean?" Nala asked.

Rafiki just hummed and turned away.

"I know," said Simba. "If we stop chasing Zinga, she'll come looking for us. All we have to do is wait where Zazu told us!"

"All right!" Nala sprinted away with Simba.

Neither of them saw Zinga flying toward the elephant's watering hole.

Simba lay back, his paws in the air. "Hey, this bird-sitting is easy. Nothing to—"

The ground began to shake. Simba and Nala stood up. The herd of elephants was stampeding toward them, with Zinga in the lead. "Run for your life!" Zinga yelled.

Simba and Nala leaped up onto some high rocks. Zinga landed near them, panting. The elephants ran past and around the rocks, their big feet crushing a

path into the ground. As
the herd moved away, Simba
and Nala frowned at Zinga.

"I didn't mean to," she said. "I was just playing with
them, you know—pulling tails." She smiled weakly. "I
didn't mean to make them stampede."

Simba pointed toward the last of the herd. "That,
Zinga, is why we wanted you to stay close to us."
Simba hoped he sounded like his father. "When you
wander off, you get into trouble."

"That's right," added Nala. Out of the side of her
mouth, she added, "You sound like Zazu."

Simba stared at her. Like Zazu?

"That is music to my ears, Nala!" Zazu said as he landed on the rocks.

"Oh, my, yes," said Zinga's mother as she joined them. "I can see why you picked these two for bird-sitting. I'm sure they don't give you any trouble."

Zazu smiled. "I'm sure they won't be giving me any trouble for a while."

Nala and Simba looked at each other and nodded. They were too tired to cause trouble—for a while.

Chow Time at the Zoo

What does a lion want for lunch? What snack might tempt a picky panda? Imagine fixing meals for thousands of different animals. They all have different needs. And not one can tell you what it wants!

That's the job that zoos face every day. Luckily, zoos have experts to help figure out what the animals need in their diets.

Zookeepers will go to any length—or height—to feed the animals in their care!

46

A baby hippo gets a bottle, just like a human baby! But most of the food served at the zoo is fixed in a special kitchen.

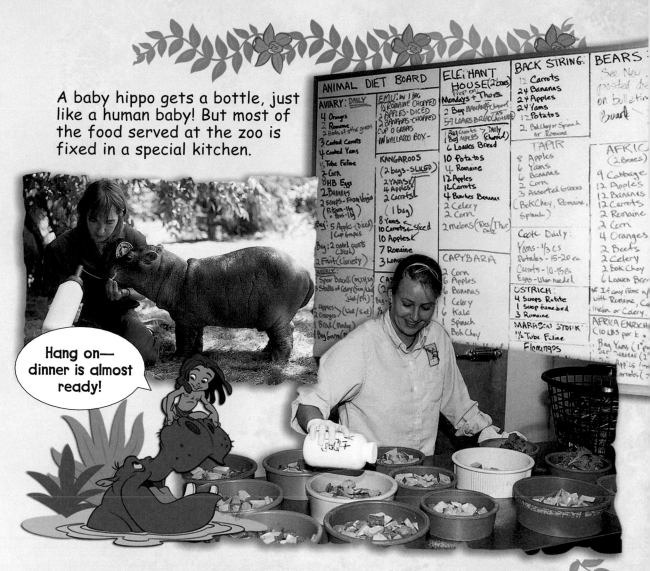

They start by looking at what the animal eats in the wild. Then they come up with a diet that has the same nutrients. Nutrients are all the things in food that the animal needs to stay healthy.

Now it's up to the zoo chefs and zookeepers. They make sure that each animal gets the foods it needs. Mice, mealworms, meat mix—they're all on the menu at the zoo!

Animals in zoos don't usually get the same foods they would in the wild. Plants a giraffe would eat in Africa don't grow in North America, for example.

47

A zoo panda shakes biscuits from a ball. Toys like this keep zoo animals from getting bored.

Instead, zoos use prepared foods. A monkey might get "Monkey Chow." An anteater might get "Instant Ant." These foods have all the necessary vitamins and minerals.

Zoos also feed little extras that the animals really enjoy. For example, monkeys get fruit and other treats as well as chow.

Please Don't Feed the Animals

If you've been to a zoo, you have seen signs telling you not to give food to the animals. Here's why:

Hundreds of people visit the zoo every day. If they all toss food to the animals, the animals will fill up on "junk" food. Just like people who snack too much, they won't be hungry at mealtime. Then they won't get the nutrients they need to stay healthy!

Grazing animals munch on foods called "browse"—plant stems and leaves. Zoos go through a lot of browse. A single elephant eats 100 pounds of hay a day, along with 30 pounds of fruits and vegetables!

Sometimes animals get special goodies. In hot weather, zoo bears may chill out with bear "popsicles." These treats are oranges frozen in a bucket of water. The bears lick and play with the pops until they can pry the oranges out of the melting ice.

Zoo experts keep a careful watch on what the animals eat. The chow they are fed should keep the animals happy and healthy. Then the zoo chefs and zookeepers know they have done a good job!

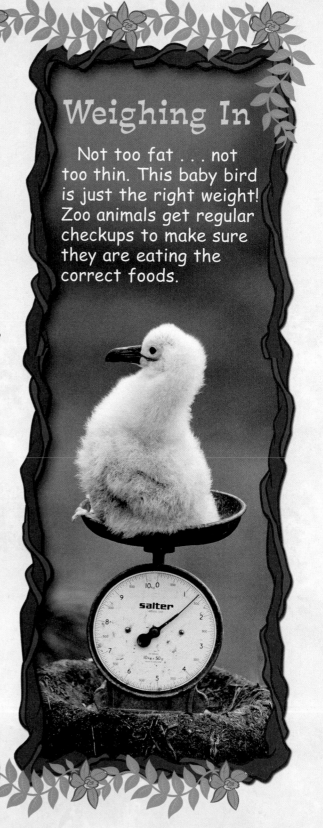

Weighing In

Not too fat . . . not too thin. This baby bird is just the right weight! Zoo animals get regular checkups to make sure they are eating the correct foods.

A mushroom makes an excellent umbrella for a little frog!

Amazing Mushrooms

This is a great place for a fairy to rest!

There's something amazing about mushrooms. They spring up overnight. And they look magical—like little umbrellas, or seats for fairies.

What are mushrooms? They aren't plants. Plants make their own food, but mushrooms do not. They aren't animals. Animals move around, but mushrooms cannot. Mushrooms belong to a different family of living things. They are fungi.

Mushrooms grow almost everywhere. Look for mushrooms in damp soil and rotting wood. You'll be surprised at what you find!

Some mushrooms are so small, you can barely see them. But some grow bigger than soccer balls! Many mushrooms are shaped like little umbrellas. Others look like cups, balls, or shelves. They may be white, brown, red, yellow, or some other color. Some mushrooms are lacy, and some even have spots!

There are hundreds of different kinds of mushrooms. Top to bottom: White-capped mushrooms are common. The lacy mushroom looks pretty but smells rotten. Golden spoon-shaped mushrooms grow in parts of the United States. Pink umbrella mushrooms grow in Central America.

Some mushrooms glow in the dark! These mushrooms make special chemicals that cause them to shine.

Many mushrooms are food for animals and people. But some mushrooms are poisonous. Only a mushroom expert can tell the difference between a safe mushroom and a deadly mushroom. That's why you should never ever eat a mushroom that you find growing wild!

Beware: These red mushrooms look pretty. But they are poisonous!

Don't pick the mushrooms, boys!

Long ago, people thought that toads made mushrooms poisonous by sitting on them. That's not true. But some people still call poisonous mushrooms "toadstools." And for these toads, mushrooms really *are* stools!

These bracket mushrooms look like shelves. They are growing from the side of a tree.

Shelves! Just the place for my fairy dust.

Make Spore Prints!

1. Find a mushroom where you can see the slits on the underside of the cap.

2. Remove the stem.

3. Put the cap, slits down, on a sheet of white paper. Cover it with a bowl and leave it overnight.

4. Lift the bowl and the mushroom. Spores will have fallen out, leaving a pattern on the paper. Now you have fungus finger-prints. And each one is different!

There's more to a mushroom than you can see. Hidden in the mushroom are tiny spores. They look like specks of dust. The spores drop from the mushroom. Wind and rain carry them away. If a spore lands on damp soil or a rotting log, it begins to grow. Soon new mushrooms push up through the soil.

And under the soil or inside the rotting log is a tangle of tiny white threads. These threads soak up the water and food that the mushroom needs to live!

Doggone It, Stitch!

Stitch was waiting for Lilo to come home from school when Lilo burst into the house, carrying a puppy.

"Hi, Stitch!" Lilo called. "My neighbor Leilani asked me to take care of her puppy, Rover, while she visits her grandmother."

"Stitch wants to listen to Elvis," Stitch said.

"Not now," Lilo answered. "I have to take care of Rover."

Stitch watched Lilo feed
Rover and make him a
bed. He watched her
scratch Rover's ears and
rub his tummy. She
wasn't paying any attention
to Stitch.

"Can we listen to Elvis now?" Stitch asked.

"I want to teach Rover some new tricks," Lilo said.

Stitch watched Lilo teach Rover to sit up and lie down.
She showed him how to roll over. She threw balls for
the puppy and gave him treats.

That evening, Nani and Lilo watched Rover play tug-of-war with the kitchen rug. "Oh, isn't he cute!" Nani exclaimed. They laughed at everything Rover did. They weren't paying any attention to Stitch.

Stitch went to bed feeling a little sad and left out. Maybe if I act like a puppy, he thought, Lilo will pay attention to me.

The next morning, Stitch tried to act like Rover. He hid Lilo's shoes and chewed the kitchen rug. But that only made Lilo angry.

"You need a time out," she told Stitch. "Go to our room while I take Rover for a walk."

Stitch waited
until Lilo and
Rover were gone.
Then he hurried
outside and ran
toward town.

When Lilo and Rover
came home, it was time for her
to go to her hula class. Lilo couldn't find
Stitch anywhere. She wondered why he wasn't home.
Stitch loved dancing the hula.

I guess I'll have to go without him, Lilo thought.

Stitch wasn't home when she returned, either. "Have you seen Stitch?" she asked Nani and her friend, David.

Before they could answer, Cobra Bubbles the social worker knocked at the door.

"You need to hide Stitch," he told them. "Two scientists from the Center for the Study of Aliens are looking for him. They want to take him to their laboratory and study him."

"But I don't know where Stitch is!" Lilo exclaimed. "He's gone!"

"Well, I suggest you find him before the scientists do," Cobra replied.

Lilo and Nani hurried to town to look for Stitch. Cobra Bubbles and David drove to the beach to look for him.

"Stitch has been acting weird all day," Lilo told Nani as they searched. "His badness level was way up. He hid my shoes and chewed the rug. He acted just like Rover!"

Suddenly, Lilo knew where Stitch had
gone. "Come on!" she shouted, grabbing
Nani's hand. "I bet Stitch thought I liked Rover
better because he was a cute puppy. I bet Stitch
went to the animal shelter to watch the puppies!"

Sure enough, when they reached the shelter, Stitch
was there.

"Stitch learning to be cute like puppy," Stitch
explained when he saw Lilo. "So Lilo like him again."

"Stitch, I like you just the way you are," Lilo
answered. "Now, let's go home!"

But when they started to
leave, they saw the two
scientists coming toward
them.

"Nani!" Lilo said. "We gotta
do something!"

Nani spotted two dust mops in
the shelter closet. She tied the dust
mops onto Stitch so he looked like a
floppy puppy.

Lilo put a leash on Stitch and, together, they walked
slowly out of the shelter and past the scientists. The
scientists watched Stitch suspiciously.

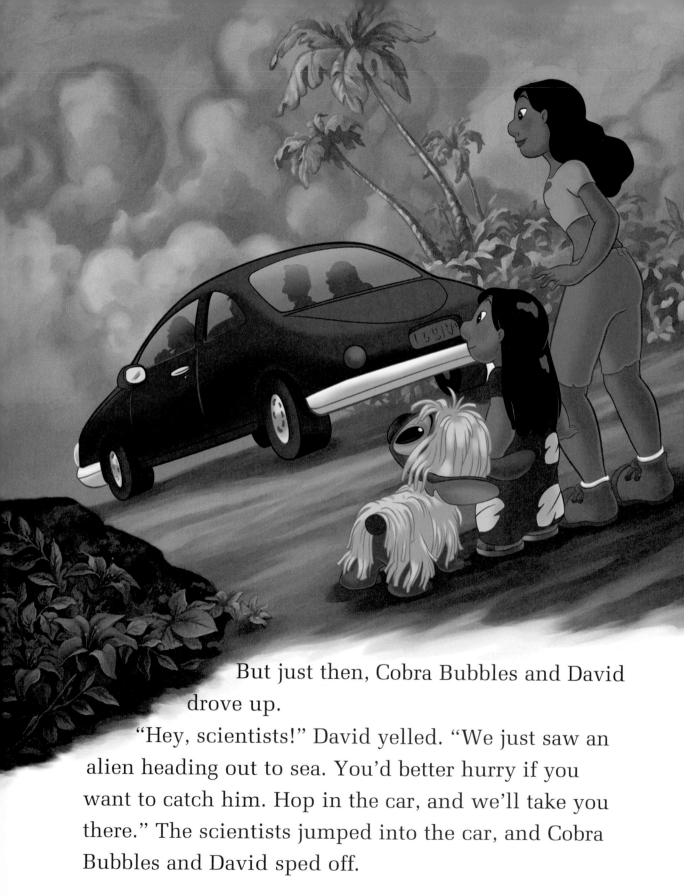

But just then, Cobra Bubbles and David
drove up.

"Hey, scientists!" David yelled. "We just saw an
alien heading out to sea. You'd better hurry if you
want to catch him. Hop in the car, and we'll take you
there." The scientists jumped into the car, and Cobra
Bubbles and David sped off.

Nani, Lilo, and Stitch were safe!

As soon as they got home, Lilo and Nani made a pink-frosted cake with the word 'ohana spelled out on top.

As they were starting to eat the cake, Cobra Bubbles and David came in. "The scientists are heading out to sea to look for Stitch," Cobra said. "He's safe for now."

"And look what I found at the beach," David said. He lifted a kitten out of a bag and set it on the floor.

"I thought she needed a good home," he said.

"How cute!" Lilo said. Stitch watched everyone play with the kitten. But before he could start to feel left out again, the kitten climbed into his lap and fell asleep. Stitch felt warm and happy inside.

"Stitch never had pet before," Stitch said. "Can Stitch keep kitten?"

"Yes," Nani answered. "In fact, I think that kitten has just adopted you as its family."

"And you know what that means," Lilo said.

Stitch nodded solemnly. "'*Ohana*. It means 'family.' And in a family, nobody—Stitch or kitten—gets left out!"

Treasure Boxes

It's fun to collect seashells. It's even more fun to use them to create these boxes. You can fill the boxes with precious treasures.

WHAT YOU NEED

Different-shaped Boxes

Small Seashells

White Glue

Colored Sand

Varnish

Paintbrushes

WHAT YOU DO

1. Spread glue on the four sides of the box. Use a paintbrush to smooth the glue out.

2. Sprinkle the colored sand onto the gluey areas. Do this over a newspaper to catch the sand that doesn't stick. Make sure the sand completely covers.

3. Spread the glue onto the top of the box. Smooth out the glue, but keep it rather thick.

4. While the glue is still wet, press the seashells into the glue. Make a nice decoration.

5. Let the box dry thoroughly. Then paint the shells with a coat of varnish, to give them a shiny finish.

6. Now fill your little treasure chest!

THE ART OF MOLAS

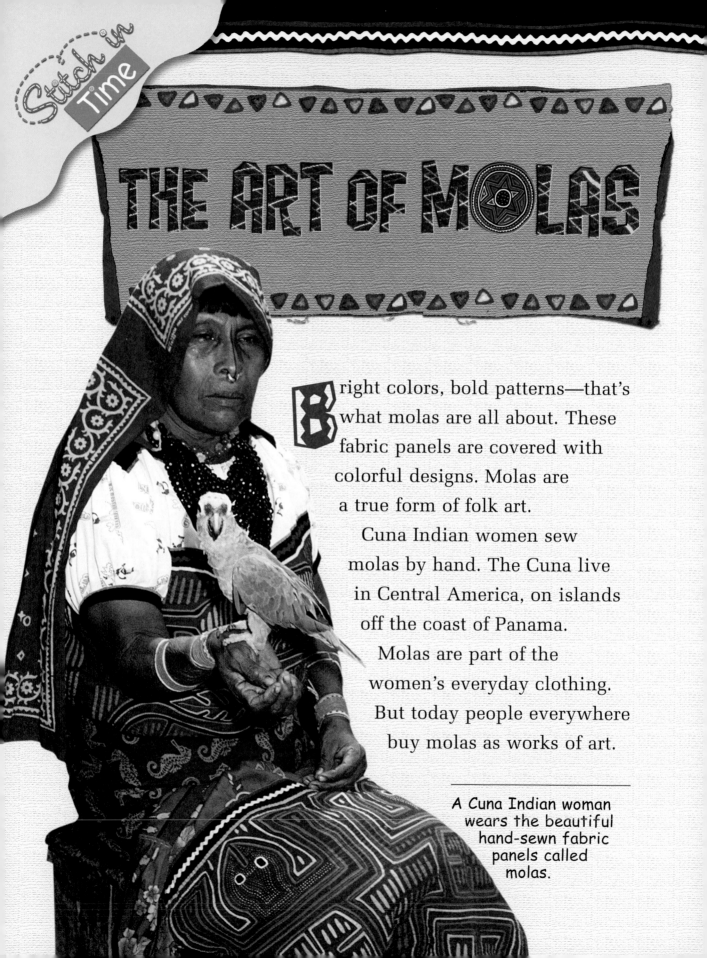

Bright colors, bold patterns—that's what molas are all about. These fabric panels are covered with colorful designs. Molas are a true form of folk art.

Cuna Indian women sew molas by hand. The Cuna live in Central America, on islands off the coast of Panama.

Molas are part of the women's everyday clothing. But today people everywhere buy molas as works of art.

A Cuna Indian woman wears the beautiful hand-sewn fabric panels called molas.

Each mola is made from many layers of different-colored cloth. First, the mola maker draws a design on the top layer of cloth.

Then the layers of cloth are carefully cut and stitched. Details are added with colored threads. It takes weeks to make each panel. A mola is like a sculpture in cloth.

Plants and animals—even imaginary ones—are often shown on molas.

This mola shows a farmer surrounded by animals. Can you spot them all?

A mola with birds . . . delightful!

Colorful parrots and a tropical fish mingle on this mola.

MOLA MAKING

Molas are made from many layers of different-colored fabrics. The maker first draws the design on the top layer. Then she carefully cuts away layers to show the colors below.

A mola could show anything—even me!

Molas can have all sorts of designs. Some molas show the plants and animals of the Cuna homeland. The rain forests and oceans of this area are a natural wonderland. And the Cuna people love their wildlife.

. . . or me!

An owl swoops over a surprised woman's shoulder in this mola.

70

Some molas show people fishing or farming. Others show scenes from history. Some show dreams. Some show folktales. And some just show circles, squares, and other shapes.

Today the Cuna also use lots of modern designs in their molas. Many of these molas are made for sale to tourists. But the most beautiful molas are the ones that the Cuna women make for themselves.

The women cover every inch of these special molas with designs. Making and wearing molas is a way for them to honor their community and their traditions.

Today, Cuna women include anything and everything in their mola designs. Magazine ads and pictures from books become subjects for many designs. Cartoon characters are also popular. Some molas even show things that the Cuna have never seen. How about snowmen and Santa Claus? Teenage Mutant Ninja Turtles? Why not!

Birdie, Be Mine!

Who is *your* Prince Charming?

These birds are in love. They're lovebirds!

Spring is the time when birds pair up to raise their families. And male birds go all out to attract females. They dance. They show off their feathers. And they do all sorts of tricks. Male birds will do almost anything to get a mate!

Show Off! A peacock wows a female with his beautiful feathers!

72

Puff Up! A male frigatebird has a red throat pouch. When a female comes near, he puffs up his pouch. She can't resist him!

Dance! A blue-footed booby dances for his mate. He hops around, flaps his wings, and whistles. It's quite a show!

Aren't birds wonderful?

Give Gifts! A male great blue heron brings his mate a stick. It's his way of showing that he can help build a good nest!

Just a Touch of Magic

King Horace and Queen Clarabelle loved to dance, and they often gave fabulous royal balls. Their daughter, Princess Daisy, however, had no interest at all in parties. True to her name, she loved flowers and plants and everything neat and pretty. She kept the royal landscapers and decorators quite busy.

One day the queen had an idea. "Daisy, dear, let's have a Beautiful Cottage Contest. You can be the judge!" she suggested.

"What fun!" Daisy exclaimed. "What will the most beautiful cottage winner win?"

The king said, "No matter how humble he is, the winner will be invited to the next ball!"

The whole kingdom was abuzz with the news. Everyone was entering the Beautiful Cottage Contest—everyone except a poor fisherman named

Donald Duck.

Donald wanted to go to the ball and dance with the princess more than anything, but he knew his humble, tumble-down cottage could never win. Those messy chipmunks Chip 'n' Dale just wouldn't stay away.

Donald didn't have much luck fishing, either. He kept seeing himself dancing with the princess. He shook himself out of his daydream. "What's that?" he said, pulling in his fishing line. An odd-looking stick dangled from the line.

"Maybe it's a magic wand! Then I can use it to win the contest and go to the ball!" He quickly rowed home.

Donald looked at the wand. "No magic words on it. I wonder how it works." He pointed it at the leaky roof and cried, "Patch the thatch!"

The roof didn't patch itself, but a huge pile of new thatch appeared. Donald spent the rest of the day re-thatching his roof.

As he crawled into bed that night, Donald tossed the wand on the table, where it landed on top of his can of blue paint. "Maybe I'll paint all the windowsills tomorrow," he muttered. "Wish I had enough paint for the shutters and door, too."

The next morning, Donald took the paintbrush and
can of blue paint from the table and tripped. "Waak!"
he cried, tumbling over five more cans of blue paint.
"Hey! There's enough blue paint for all the trim! My
magic wand is still working!"

By the end of the afternoon, his roof, windowsills,
shutters, and door definitely looked a lot brighter.
Unfortunately, the dull gray walls just looked duller
and grayer.

"What I need is whitewash!" Donald cried. Trying magic again, he used the wand—and a large tub of whitewash appeared. Then he found an old broom for a brush. Donald sighed and set to work. "Wish I had a couple more hands and brooms for this job."

After a few minutes, he heard a familiar chattering. "Not again!" he said when he saw Chip 'n' Dale. Each was holding a pint-sized broom dripping with whitewash. Donald smiled. Instead of causing trouble, the two chipmunks were gleefully dabbing whitewash on the cottage walls.

When Donald and the
chipmunks had finally
covered every dingy spot
with whitewash, all three
of them were as white as
the cottage walls.

Donald ran to the lake and
washed off. Sputtering and
dripping, he looked up at his
cottage. The new thatch, the blue trim, and the
whitewashed walls looked even better—except for the

speckles of whitewash on the bushes. Donald ran inside and tossed the wand onto the table. It landed on a pair of pruning shears.

After Donald changed into dry clothes, he noticed a sparkle on the pruning shears. As he picked them up, the wand rolled off the table and landed on Donald's wet clothes.

Outside, Donald started snipping. Snip, snip here. Snip, snip there. It was almost as if the shears were snipping on their own.

Suddenly the snipping stopped. "Waak!" Donald cried. "That bush looks like me! And that one looks like Princess Daisy!" Donald would have fainted then and there, but he heard trumpets blaring. Princess Daisy was coming!

Donald raced inside to look for some clean clothes. Much to his surprise, he found some under the wand. But then he saw the dirty dishes, clothes, and dust everywhere, along with Chip 'n' Dale's dirty paw prints. "I sure wish the inside was as pretty as the outside," he said with a sigh. Tossing the wand on the floor, he went outside to greet the princess.

Donald bowed as Princess Daisy descended from the royal carriage. "What a sweet cottage," she said.

"Thank you, Your Princess-ness." Donald took off his hat and bowed.

"New thatch," the princess quietly said. "Fresh whitewashing. Trim painted my favorite shade of blue!" Then Princess Daisy saw the bushes. "Oh!" she cried. "Is that. . .? And that. . .? Why, how delightful!" Donald blushed. "Donald, you have almost won the Beautiful Cottage Contest! All I need is a peek inside your sweet, humble cottage."

"Oh, no, Your Princess-ness, you don't really want to
see the inside of my cottage. Not sweet. Too humble.
Too . . . late."

Princess Daisy had opened the door. "What?" cried
Donald.

"Delightful!" she said. "I love it! The furniture—
Chippendale, isn't it?"

Neither of them heard a fairy's voice outside. "So
that's where you are, you naughty wand! Come on . . ."
The wand floated out the window.

84

The next time Donald heard trumpets blaring, they were for him! He arrived at the ball in a brand-new suit of clothes. And Donald Duck, a humble fisherman, danced at the ball with Princess Daisy all night long.

Let's meet Sister Act

You go, girl!

Serena and Venus: sisters, tennis stars, best friends.

No one can hit a tennis ball like Venus Williams. Well, no one but her sister Serena! Venus and Serena Williams are top stars in women's tennis. And these winning sisters are best friends, too.

Venus and Serena have been playing tennis since they were four years old. Playing singly, each sister has won major tennis titles. And when they play as a team, the Williams sisters are hard to beat!

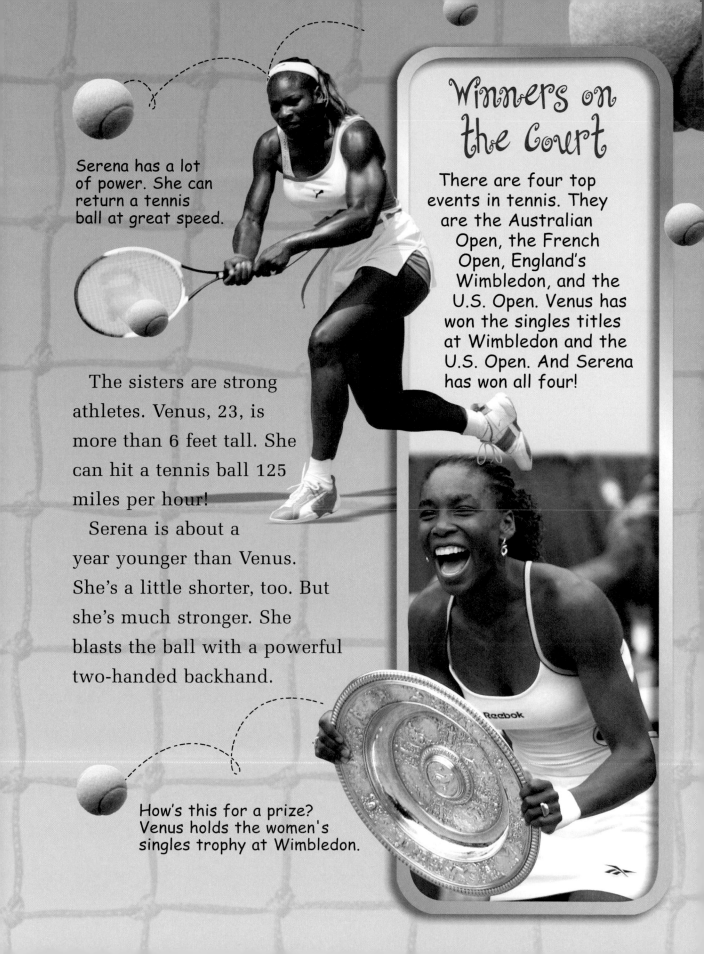

Serena has a lot of power. She can return a tennis ball at great speed.

There are four top events in tennis. They are the Australian Open, the French Open, England's Wimbledon, and the U.S. Open. Venus has won the singles titles at Wimbledon and the U.S. Open. And Serena has won all four!

The sisters are strong athletes. Venus, 23, is more than 6 feet tall. She can hit a tennis ball 125 miles per hour!

Serena is about a year younger than Venus. She's a little shorter, too. But she's much stronger. She blasts the ball with a powerful two-handed backhand.

How's this for a prize? Venus holds the women's singles trophy at Wimbledon.

Growing Up

Sisters and pals: On the tennis court as kids (top). With beaded braids and braces as teens (middle). At a fashion awards show in their twenties (bottom).

Venus and Serena are rivals on the tennis court. But off the court they are very close. They practice together and enjoy many of the same activities.

The girls grew up in California and Florida. They have three older sisters. Venus and Serena started playing tennis as kids.

The sisters say their close family life has helped them succeed in professional tennis. Their parents usually travel with them, and their dad has been their coach.

But they know there's more to life than tennis. Venus and Serena are both interested in careers in fashion design. Serena is also thinking about an acting career.

Venus and Serena are double trouble on the tennis court. That must be why they were asked to do ads for this chewing gum!

When the Williams sisters were growing up, Venus helped her younger sister Serena learn the game of tennis. But now Serena is more than a match for her big sister. And when Venus and Serena face each other in a tennis game, Serena usually wins.

Fans pack the stands when the Williams sisters are on the court. People love to watch these amazing sisters in action!

Those sisters . . . what dolls!

The Williams sisters are so famous, there are even Venus and Serena dolls!

PERFECT PARTNERS

Clownfish and sea anemones have a special relationship. Each gets something from the other.

Uh-oh! This playground is only for clownfish—not flounders!

FISHY FRIENDS

A sea anemone looks like a flower, but it's really an animal. The anemone has lots of arms that look just like petals. But if a fish runs into those arms, they sting! However, there is one fish—the clownfish—that can live right among the anemone's arms! This fish gobbles up tiny bits of ocean food that's trapped there. The fish gets a meal. The anemone gets a cleaning. They are partners.

90

CLEANER CHUMS

There are many more animal partners. And some of them make very odd couples! But working together helps them survive. For example, like sea anemones, lots of fish can't groom themselves. They count on other animals to help. And like the clownfish, the groomers get a meal.

Little groomers like the cleaner wrasse (above) and the cleaner shrimp (below) aren't afraid of their big partners!

BIRD BUDDIES

Birds called egrets like to hang out with big animals like this African rhinoceros. They are looking for a meal! As the rhino stomps through the grass, it startles insects. The insects fly up to get out of the way. And the egrets eat the insects. The rhino gets something out of the partnership, too. If the egrets see danger, they warn the rhino. They call out, flap their wings, and even hop up on the big animal's back.

Hey, can I hitch a ride?

ON GUARD

Oxpeckers are tiny African birds that help out in a very big way. They eat ticks that they pluck from the fur of large animals. Besides keeping the animals free of pests, they also warn of danger. An oxpecker will even sit on its big buddy's head and peck, peck, peck to make its point!

An oxpecker spends most of its life riding around on a big animal such as an antelope (above) or a buffalo (below). The bird even sleeps on its animal!

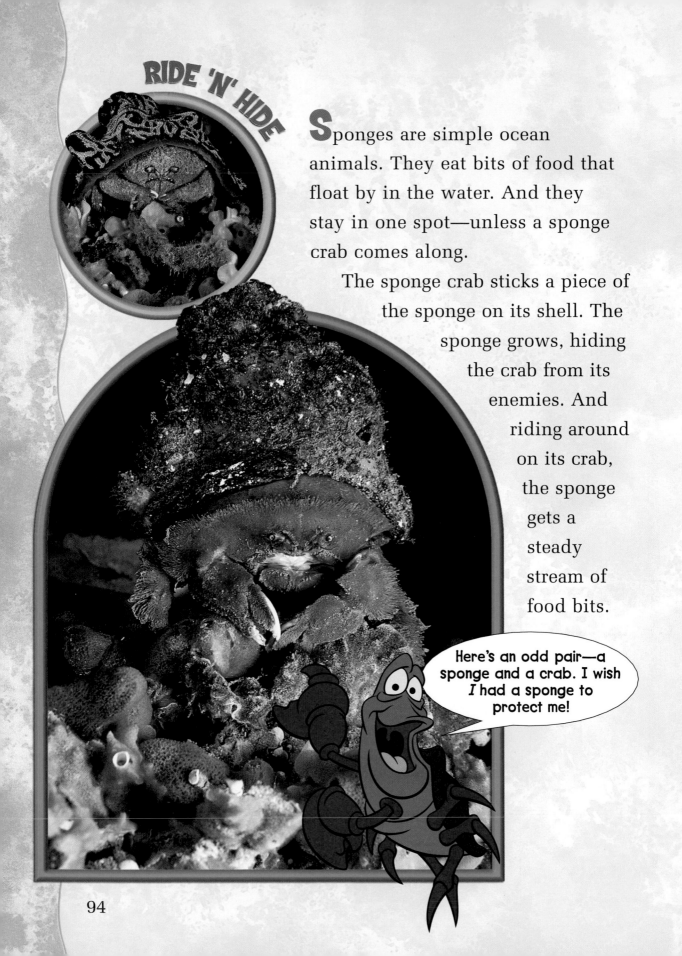

RIDE 'N' HIDE

Sponges are simple ocean animals. They eat bits of food that float by in the water. And they stay in one spot—unless a sponge crab comes along.

The sponge crab sticks a piece of the sponge on its shell. The sponge grows, hiding the crab from its enemies. And riding around on its crab, the sponge gets a steady stream of food bits.

Here's an odd pair—a sponge and a crab. I wish *I* had a sponge to protect me!

94

SWEET DEALS

Aphids are tiny insects. You can find them on garden plants, on stems and under leaves. They feed by sucking juice from the plants. And they make a sweet substance called honeydew.

Ants love honeydew. To get it, some ants tend aphids the way people tend cows! The ants guard the little insects and move them to good feeding spots. In exchange, the ants collect the honeydew from the aphids. Like other animal partnerships, it's a sweet deal for both!

The Last Laugh!

What does a hippo have if its head is hot and it sees spots?

A polka-dotted sock over its head!

What did the sunken ship say when it was surrounded by sharks?

Help! I'm a nervous wreck!

What did the beaver say when it heard a chain saw?

They're playing my song!

Why do mother kangaroos hate rainy days?

Because their children have to play inside!

Why didn't the skeleton go to the ball?

It had no-body to go with!

What's a sheep's favorite fruit?

Baaa-nanas!

What did the Cinderella fish wear to the ball?

Glass flippers!